W9-BZT-154

3-Dimensional
LATERAL
LOGIC MAZES

LARRY EVANS

Sterling Publishing Co., Inc.   New York

To Jeremy Evans and Plato
for their contributions
to the world of mazes

Library of Congress Cataloging-in-Publication Data

Evans, Larry 1939-
    3-dimensional lateral logic mazes / Larry Evans.
       p.   cm.
    Includes index.
    ISBN 0-8069-9624-2
    1. Maze puzzles. 2. Lateral logic. 3. Visual perception.
I. Title.
GV1507.M3E92   1997
793.73—dc21   96-48270
                                                CIP

2 4 6 8 10 9 7 5 3 1

Published by Sterling Publishing Company, Inc.
387 Park Avenue South, New York, N.Y. 10016
© 1997 by Larry Evans
Distributed in Canada by Sterling Publishing
c/o Canadian Manda Group, One Atlantic Avenue, Suite 105
Toronto, Ontario, Canada M6K 3E7
Distributed in Great Britain and Europe by Cassell PLC
Wellington House, 125 Strand, London WC2R 0BB, England
Distributed in Australia by Capricorn Link (Australia) Pty Ltd.
P.O. Box 6651, Baulkham Hills, Business Centre, NSW 2153, Australia
Manufactured in the United States of America
All rights reserved

Sterling ISBN 0-8069-9624-2

CONTENTS

Introduction   4

In the Beginning   6

Spatial Textures   14

Plato's Solids   22

Hidden Assets   30

Two for One   36

3-D Doozies   42

Two Last Puzzles
     & the Parts Department   48

The Solutions   53

Index   64

INTRODUCTION

Puzzles have a funny way of taking over your life. Just when you think you're through with them, they come out of nowhere and force you to deal with them—on their own terms! Many years ago, probably before you were born, I created a series of 3-dimensional mazes. I really liked traditional mazes but felt they were a little too easy to solve. They also had a similarity to them that made them appear to be architectural plans of mazes instead of mazes themselves. As an architectural illustrator, I had to interpret architects' drawings and create an illustration of their buildings in three dimensions. So why not do the same thing with mazes?

And so I did. Many books and posters were printed and my idea lived a good life and was buried with honors. Later on, most likely after you were born, my mazes came back to life and said (as a group), "We could be fun again if you would just make us a little more challenging—and maybe harder. Maybe you could use one of these computers we've heard about here in maze heaven."

Now, you may think it's strange to have your long-dead mazes talk to you from the grave, but that's what happens to puzzle makers. The puzzles in this book all have a 3-dimensional feel to them. Some are actually illustrated to appear to be 3-dimensional and some require you to jump from the page or visualize an object in three dimensions. In any case, just be glad they're still in the third dimension. The fourth dimension is yet to come and you'll want to be ready for it!

Happy puzzling.

1: BLOW OUT

This is a basic 3-dimensional maze. The pipes are channel tubes that float in perspective over and under each other. Enter the maze at the WHITE ball and crawl and through the tubes to the BLACK ball. There is more than one solution, but if you can't find any, the solutions are in the back of the book, introduced on page 53.

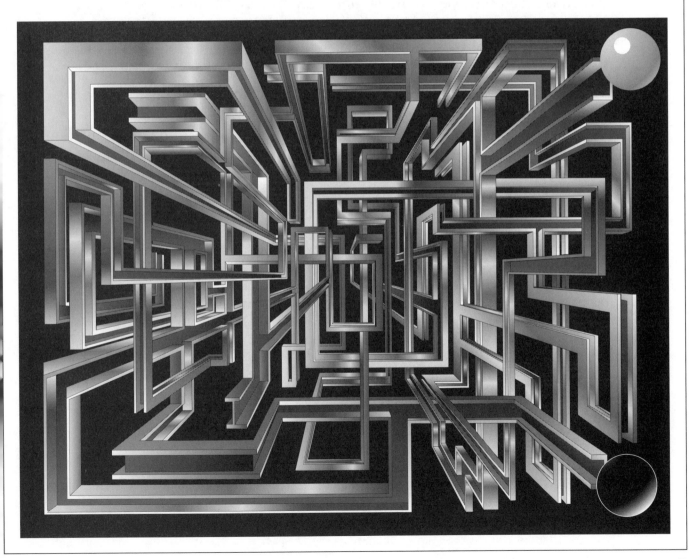

IN THE BEGINNING

In *Lateral Logic Mazes for the Serious Puzzler* (Sterling, 1996) I have a puzzle entitled "In the Beginning." It is based on an old puzzle concept which is based on an even older concept, which is, "Things are only as hard as you percieve them to be." That's possibly from Plato, who figures prominently in this book, or possibly I just made it up. In any case, this section has within its walls a few puzzles that easily fit the concept.

The first puzzle in this section is, as usual, a trick puzzle. You are asked to enter a pipe and flow from ball to ball. On the way you must touch a few black cubes and, of course, the illustration is an optical illusion, but the task sure looks easy. Ah, perception! This puzzle is so hard it will fry your brain. All the puzzles in this section are either easy or hard. I personally think the book's two hardest puzzles are in this group of five mazes. I also think that two of the easiest puzzles are here, too.

Puzzle six, the "Inside-out Cube," is so difficult to visualize, this old puzzle master himself had to build a model (in three dimensions) to even figure out how to create the beast. The idea is simply an empty box with a maze pattern an all the sides, inside and out. But something happens when you try to visualize all the parts together.

Some of these puzzles have pieces missing. You will be able to find these "pieces" in the Parts Store or the Parts Store Annex, pages 50 and 51, just prior to the Solutions.

Well, have fun with this group of mazes and we'll see you at "Spatial Textures."

2: STRUCTURE IMPOSSIBLE

Work your way through the construction from globe to globe. On your way, try to travel through each BLACK cube only once. You may not retrace your path but you MAY return to the starting cube as often as you like.

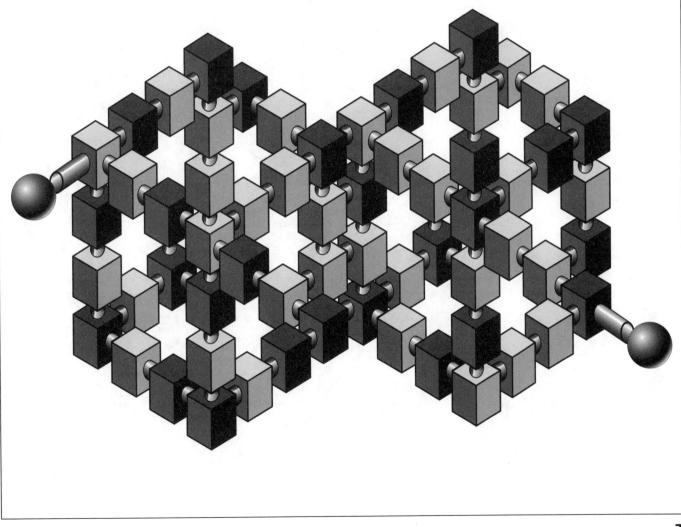

3: CUBED CUBES

Proceed from one globe to the other globe, staying within the pipes and boxes. Four boxes with their attached pipes are missing and may be found in the Parts Store.

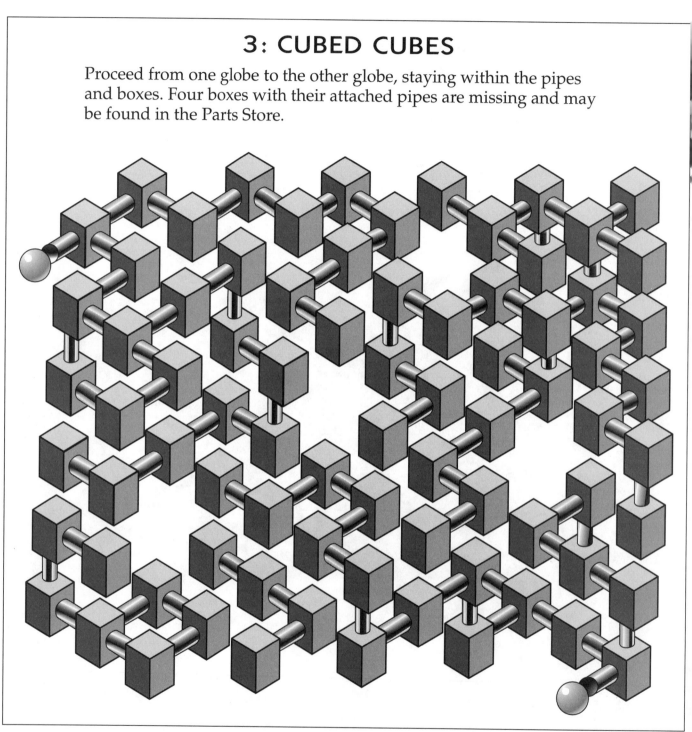

4: TWIN CUBES

Travel from DARK ball to DARK ball. If you reach a WHITE ball you must restart your journey again at the opposite DARK ball. Stay within the tubes as they cross over and under each other.

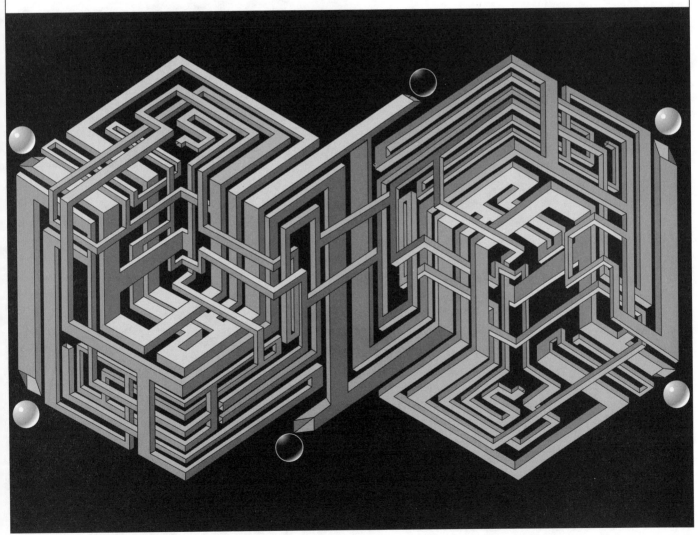

5: THE CUBIC HOTEL

Your room is the BLACK cubicle in the east wing of the hotel. To save money, the developers have eliminated the hallways from this hostelry. Enter the correct entry door and find the way to your room.

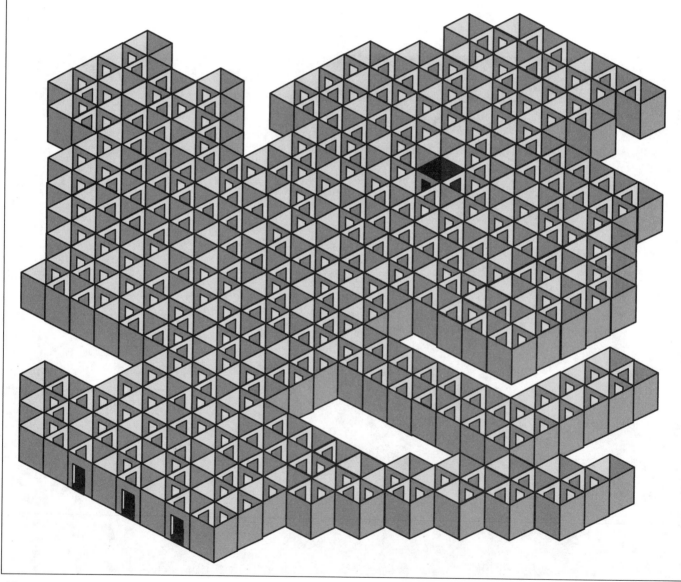

6: INSIDE-OUT CUBE

The illustration below shows all of the sides of a cube with one of its six sides removed. The maze path runs over and under itself from arrow to arrow, inside and out, over the remaining ten surfaces. Find the correct path.

7: CUBE MADNESS

The nine cubes in this puzzle have 15 sides showing. Some of the sides are in the correct place and some are not. To solve this maze, rearrange the incorrect sides and then travel from arrow to arrow as the path winds over and under itself.

8: FRACTURED FRACTILS

Enter the maze at the IN arrow and follow the path as it winds over and under itself to the OUT arrow. The two missing pieces may be found in the Parts Store.

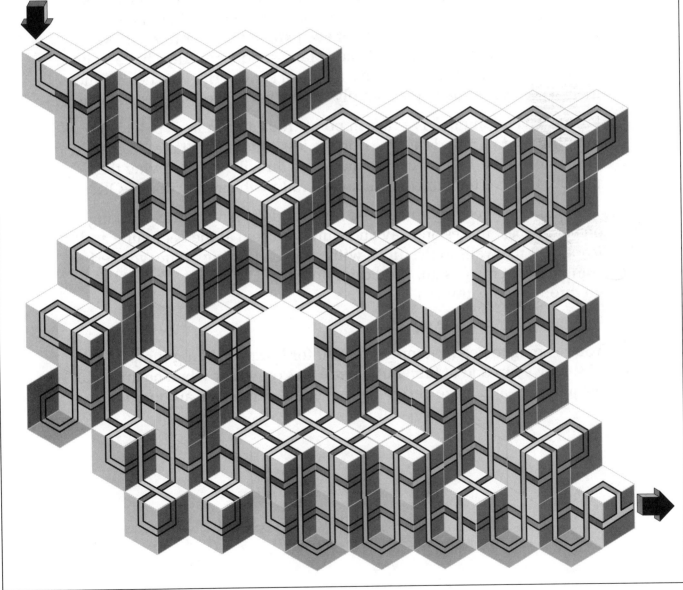

SPATIAL TEXTURES

One of the secrets to solving these puzzles is to follow directions. This task is not always easy for the serious puzzler. The idea that there might be a hidden solution, one not even known to the puzzle maker himself, is a tough concept to shake. Many serious puzzlers have written to me with alternate solutions, a tone of superiority couched within their sentences. Usually they simply have not followed the instructions.

Puzzle 9, "Frog Jump," is a case in point. You can run from ball to ball jumping over pyramids and be done in less time than it takes to change a channel on the TV. You can do that, but you will not be solving the puzzle. To solve the puzzle you have to follow the instructions—OK?

This silliness all comes up because my grandson Jeremy was working one of my best mazes one day and simply started at the beginning and leapt over the walls to the finish without even looking at the wonderful complexity of my design. "You can't do that," I hollered! "You didn't go through the pathways."

"I've got a jumper," he replied.

You're going to need a jumper yourself for Puzzle 9, "Frog Jump." The idea may seem odd at first, but Jeremy was only four when he invented the jumper—and maze design has never been the same around here.

9: FROG JUMP

Begin at any ball and continue along the paths. When you reach a pyramid you must first jump over the pyramid, landing on the ball next in line. The next time you return to the pyramid you must touch it and move on to the next ball in line. Touch all the balls and pyramids without retracing your path or touching any ball or pyramid more than once.

10: PIPE DOWN

Enter at the WHITE ball and travel through the pipes, touching ALL the balls once. You may not retrace your steps as you return to the WHITE ball. You may add TWO connecting pipes to solve this puzzle if you need them.

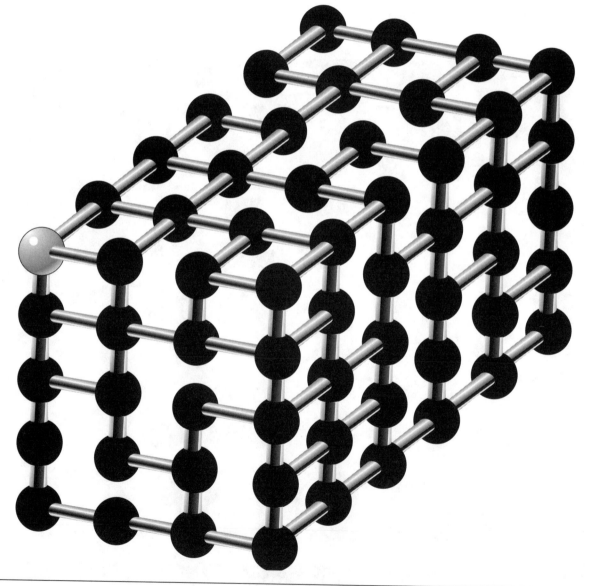

11: BALL, PYRAMID & CUBE

From the IN arrow find a path that touches all the objects only once before exiting. You must alternate between objects (ball–pyramid–cube, or ball–cube–pyramid) as you travel along your route. You must maintain the same sequence you began with throughout your journey.

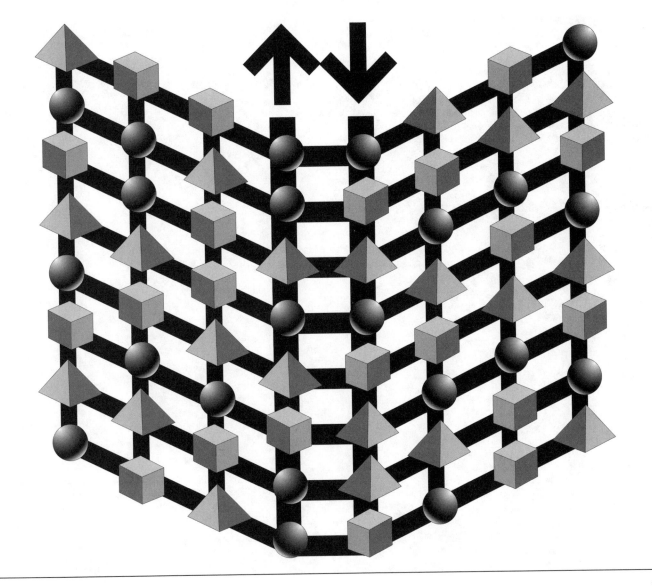

12: PLATO'S REVENGE

Begin at a WHITE ball, follow the path, touching Plato's regular solids in order (tetrahedron–cube–dodecahedron–icosahedron); then touch a DARK ball. Repeat until you have touched ALL the objects, then exit at the other WHITE ball. You may not touch any object more than once or retrace your path. You must maintain the sequence throughout your journey. You must change one solid object to a four-sided solid to solve the maze.

13: PYRAMID POWER

This pyramid is open at the bottom, allowing the maze path to meander inside and out. The inside is shown in position but the exterior needs rearrangement. Put the pieces together and follow the path as it travels over and under itself from IN to OUT.

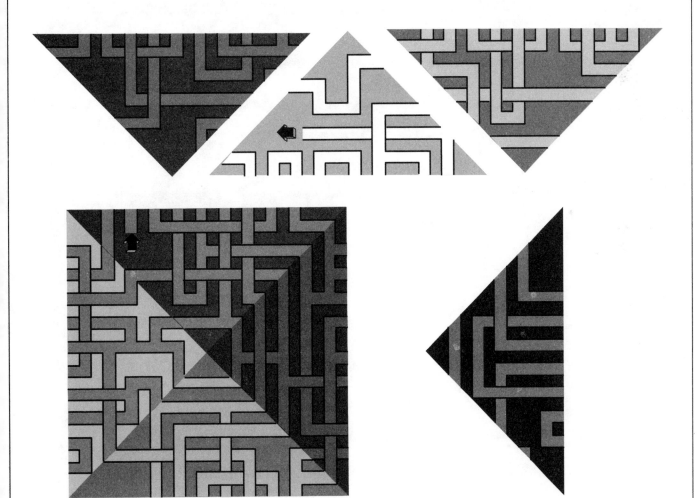

14: IN AND OUT

Starting at the BLACK pyramid, crawl through the pipes, touching all the solid objects in sequence (pyramid–ball–cube or pyramid–cube–ball). Then exit at the BLACK pyramid. You may not retrace your steps or touch any object more than once. You must also maintain the sequence you began with.

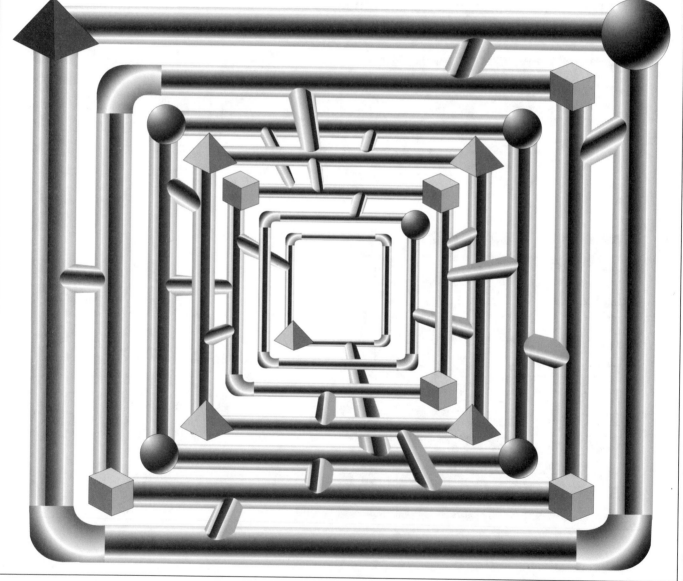

15: ROUND AND AROUND

The BLACK ball is the place to begin your trip into the maze. Exit at the WHITE ball. The missing section may be found in the Parts Store or its Annex.

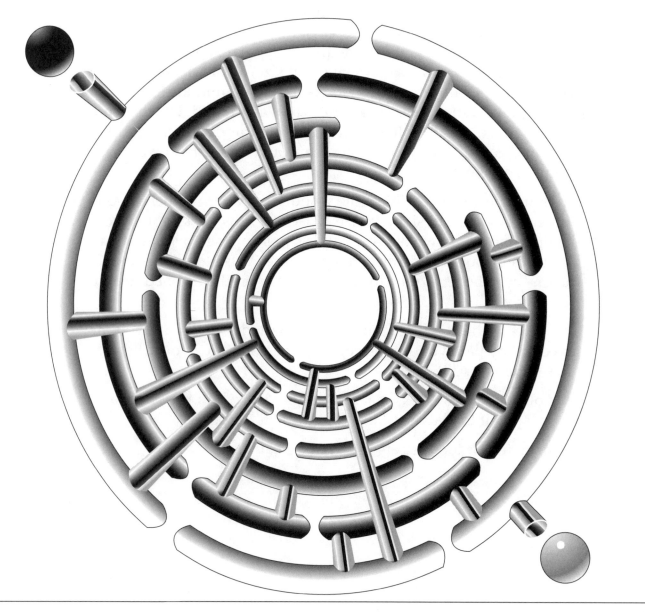

PLATO'S SOLIDS

Plato, a man who should need no introduction, formulated a theory that there could be only five regular solids: tetrahedron, cube, octahedron, dodecahedron, and icosahedron. A regular solid is faced with regular polygons of the same shape and size, all faces meeting at equal convex angles. The tetrahedron looks like a pyramid in elevation, so in this book we sometimes call a tetrahedron a pyramid, which technically is incorrect, but Plato has been gone from this earth for a couple of thousand years or so, and I'm sure he would understand what we're trying to say here.

Anyhow, these solid forms create wonderful patterns when used in 3-dimensional maze design. Puzzle 17, "Cube Plus," asks you to connect the dots and draw two of these solids superimposed over each other. Even when you see the finished item in the Parts Store (or Annex, as the case may be) it is quite difficult to construct the finished item in perspective.

The tubes in these constructions are connected by balls and you may leave on any path you like (except the one you rode in on) after you have entered a ball.

This puzzle maker thinks that a ball should also be a regular solid, so we will add it to Plato's list just for our own purposes.

Then, on to "Hidden Assets" and have a ball.

16: BREAK-OUT

Commence your voyage at the IN arrow and continue through the WHITE pipes to the OUT arrow. You may not travel through the BLACK pipes.

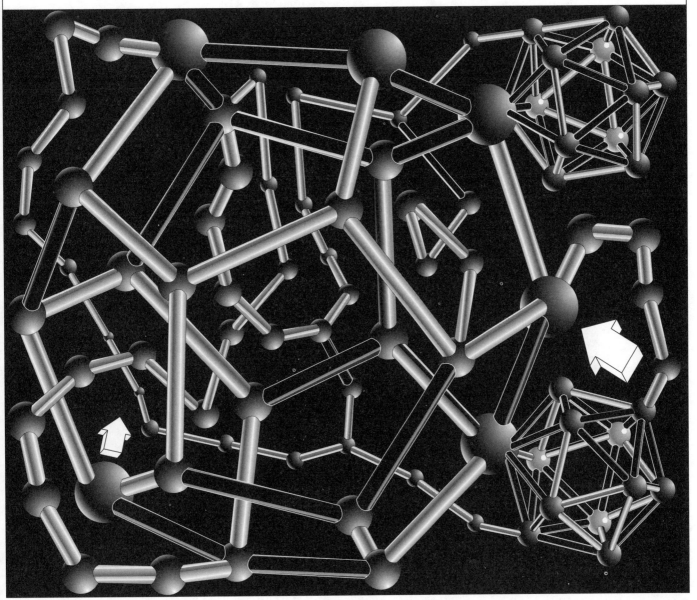

17: CUBE PLUS

Can you connect the planets with straight lines to create a transparent cube + octahedron? Two planets have been joined with a line just to get you started. You might just check in the Parts Store Annex to see one of these things.

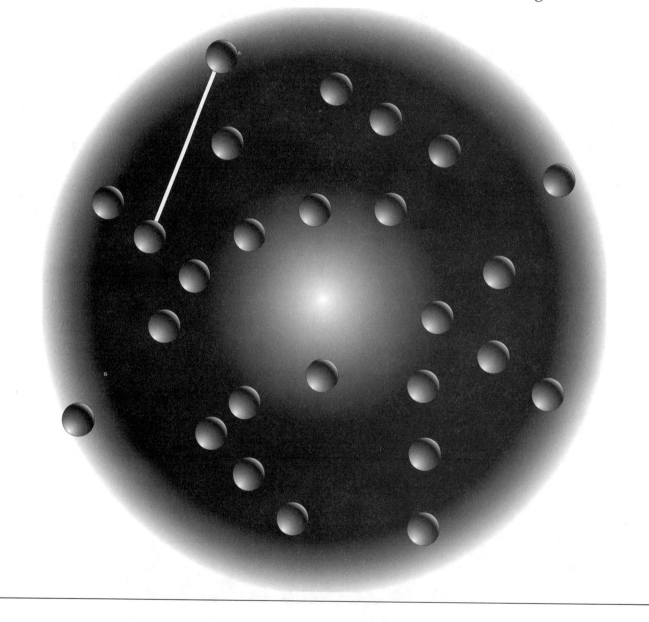

18: ICOSADODECA

Access the maze at the IN arrow and wander through the pipes until you reach the OUT arrow. Find the missing icosahedron (or is it a dodecahedron?) to complete the maze.

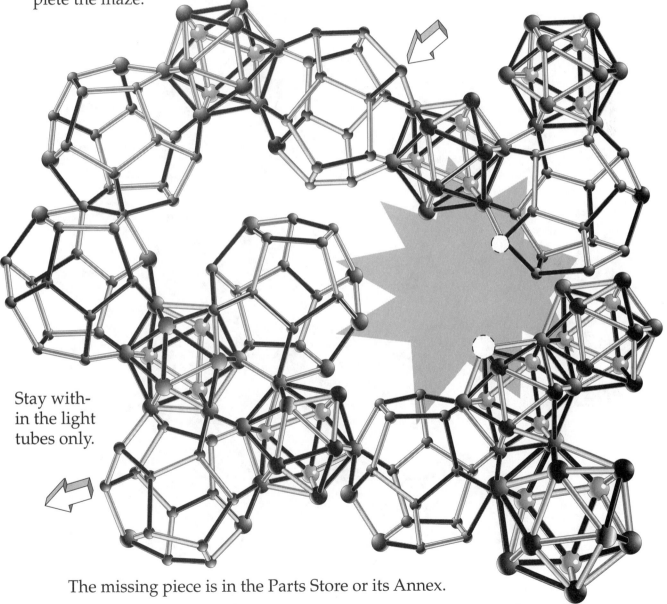

Stay within the light tubes only.

The missing piece is in the Parts Store or its Annex.

19: ICOSAHEDRON TRAILS

Begin at the IN arrow and travel within the BLACK tubes only to the OUT arrow. Then JUMP to the next page and enter the maze at the IN arrow and travel through the WHITE tubes only to the OUT arrow. The missing icosahedron may be found in the Parts Store or its Annex.

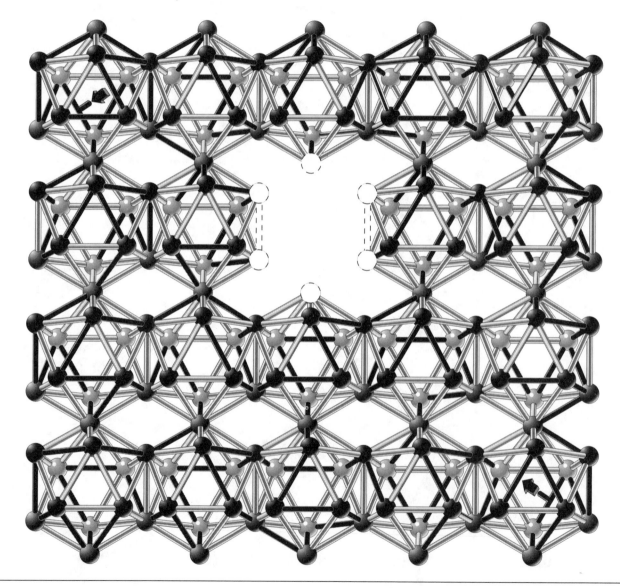

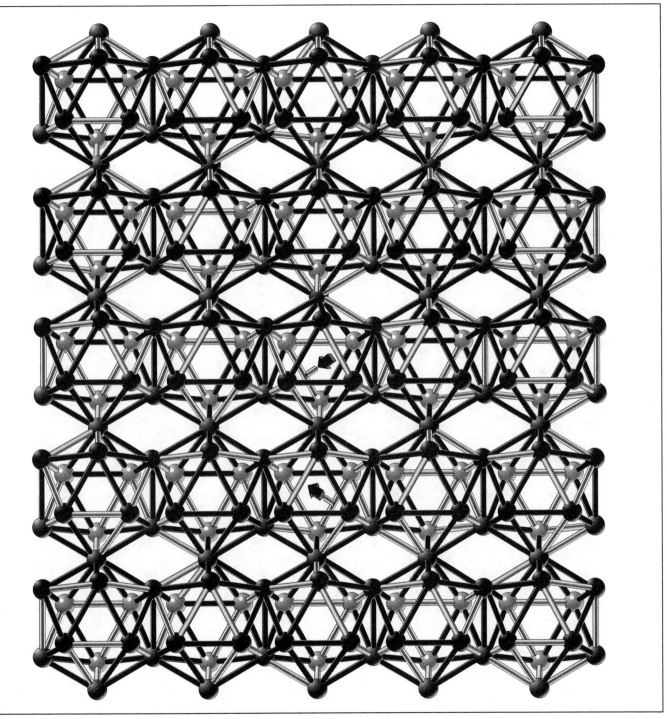

20: DODECAHEDRONS

Begin at the IN arrow and travel on the BLACK paths only. You must touch all the CUBES before exiting at the OUT arrow. You may not retrace your path or touch any ball or cube more than once, but you may leave a cube on any untraveled BLACK path. Two WHITE paths need to be changed to BLACK to solve the puzzle.

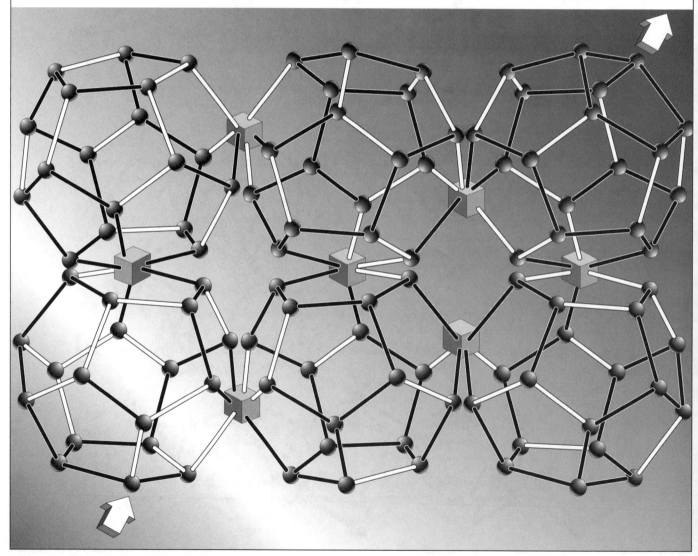

21: THE ICOSAHEDRON

The maze path has been etched on the glass sides of this icosahedron. Your job, if you choose to accept it, is to follow the path from the IN arrow to the OUT arrow as it flows over and under itself. The piece that has been removed is either alongside the icosahedron or in the Parts Store or its Annex.

HIDDEN ASSETS

This section comprises five classic 3-dimensional mazes. The paths are hollow tubes and you're invited to crawl through the pipes from a starting point to a finish in order to solve the puzzle. A few alterations, however, have been made to these classic labyrinths. In every instance a piece has been removed and sent to the Parts Store or its Annex.

Why, you might ask, would someone do such a thing? These puzzles are quite hard enough without this rude removal. Not so! As puzzle one in this book, "Blow Out," adequately illustrates, once you get into one of these mazes, eventually you must come out. Only a tiny bit of that kind of puzzle gets into the company of a 3-dimensional lateral logic maze.

A major problem for some puzzle solvers attempting a 3-dimensional maze is understanding the concept of one pipe or tube disappearing behind another. The former must often travel for some distance before becoming visible again from behind the latter. All these puzzles obey the basic rule of puzzle fairness: no hidden agendas. If the pipe looks as if it should pass all the way behind its companion, then the pipe does pass behind its companion.

You should be able to solve these puzzles quickly and then pass on to "Two for One."

22: TRY ANGLES

Crawl into the pipes at either triangle and wend your way to the other triangle. The missing piece may be found in the Parts Store or its Annex.

23: THE MISSING LINK

Enter the pipes at the IN arrow and stay within the tubes as they pass over and under each other. When you reach the OUT arrow you will be free to leave. The missing section may be found in the Parts Store.

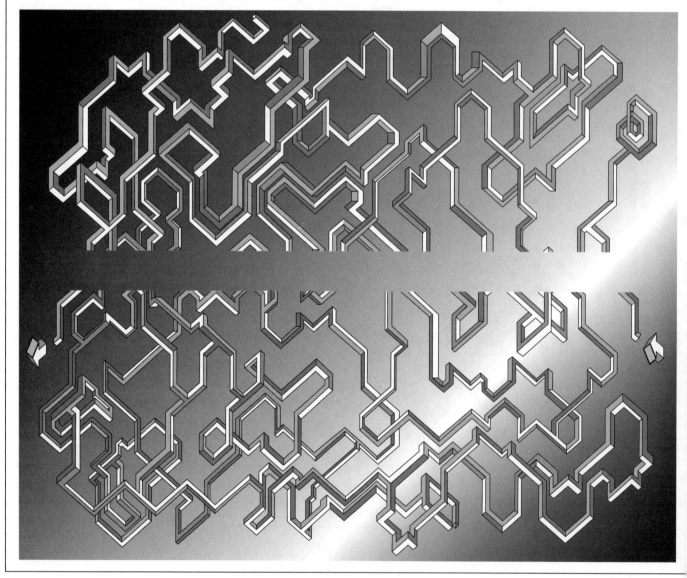

24: AROUND THE SQUARE

Travel from the ball through the pipes as they cross over and under each other and then back to the ball. The missing piece may be found in the Parts Store or its Annex. The object you're looking for may NOT be right-side up!

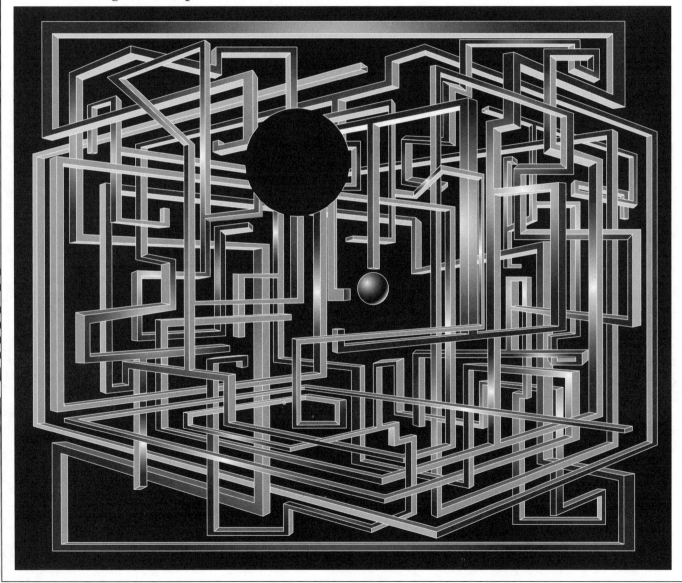

25: CIRCLE IN THE SQUARE

Enter at the IN arrow and stay within the pipes until you reach the OUT arrow. Oh, by the way, the center section of this maze has been removed and flipped upside down, but that should be no problem for a serious puzzler.

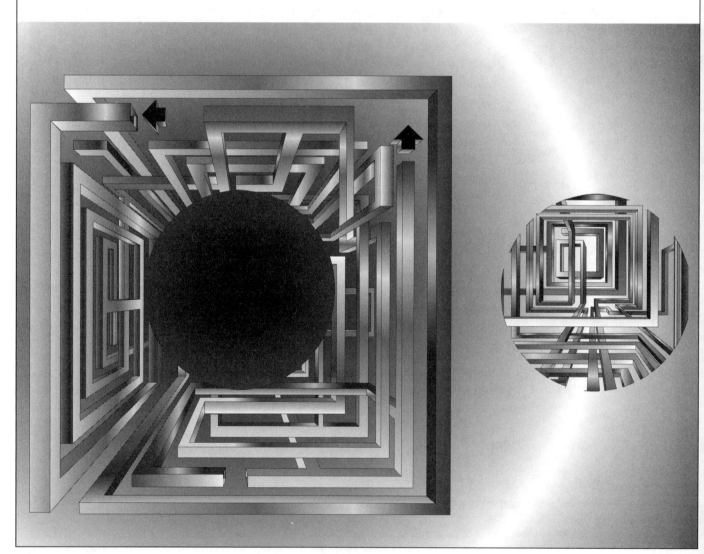

26: BALL DIAMOND

Start at the WHITE ball and enter the pipes as they flow over and under each other. Exit at the BLACK ball. The missing section is in the Parts Store or its Annex.

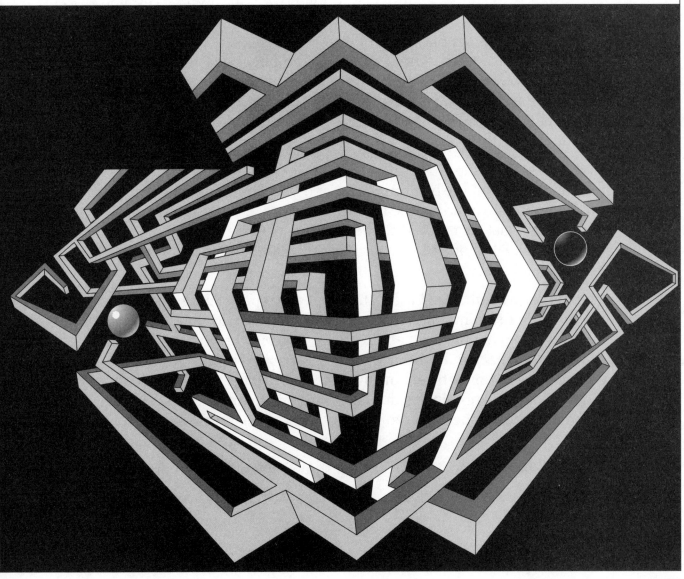

TWO FOR ONE

Often puzzles will test your ability to do more than one thing at a time. For instance, in chess you must not only move your own pieces, you must also consider all the possible moves your opponent might make. In baseball you must play both offense and defense. In each case you are asked to take your individual skills a bit beyond. This series of five puzzles asks you to solve a maze and win at Tic-Tac-Toe simultaneously. You are asked to solve a maze and exit within a set number of moves and, finally, you must put together a jigsaw puzzle while also completing the labyrinth.

In the case of Puzzle 27, "Tic-Tac-Toe," the **X** placed in the tally box represents the **X** from the beginning star. Now, it's possible that you might not know that by reading the rules of the puzzle. But you've read it here. This is just a small test to see if you're reading this important information. Kind of a puzzle within a puzzle within a . . . well you know what I mean.

Pythagoras hypothesized that "the point is to spatial magnitude what the number **1** is to number." We can only say amen to that theory. After all, isn't that what life is all about? Plato rejected the notion of a point as fiction, so that is why we use his regular solids in this book. Of course none of this is true. I mean some of it is true, but the part about Plato's point has nothing to do with using his regular solids. They're just really cool shapes and work really well in creating 3-dimensional logic mazes.

Well, I certainly hope you've learned something here. See you at "3-D Doozies."

27: TIC-TAC-TOE

Begin at any of the four outside stars and journey to the central (**X**) by alternating your moves from (**X**) to (**O**). After touching the central (**X**), travel to a different star and exit the maze. After each move mark an (**X**) or (**O**) in the Tic-Tac-Toe tally box (the first **X** has been placed for you from the beginning star). You must make all eight moves to fill the tally box and you must WIN the Tic-Tac-Toe game on your final move. Now leave from your final destination and travel to any exterior star without touching any circles already touched or traveling on any path already used. Then, complete another Tic-Tac-Toe box using the (**X**) in the destination star as the winning move.

TALLY BOX

TALLY BOX

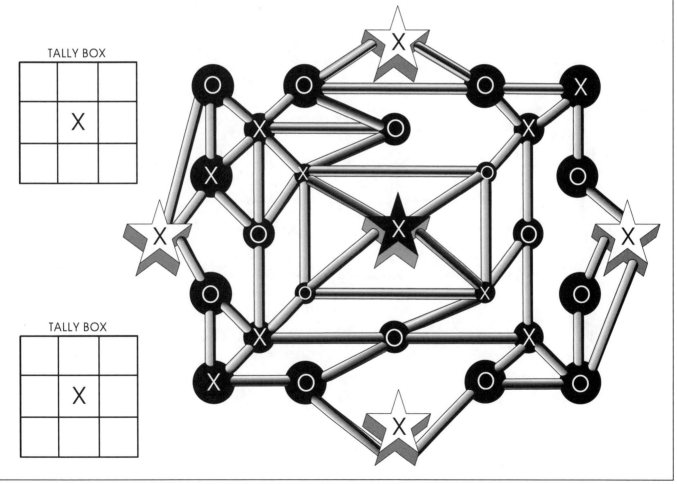

28: AROUND ABOUT

Begin at any BLACK pyramid and travel through the maze, alternating between pyramid–ball–cube or ball–cube–pyramid. Mark off a square in the tally box each time you move. Exit the maze at a BLACK pyramid at the end of the 10th sequence. Once you select a sequence you must stick with it until the end.

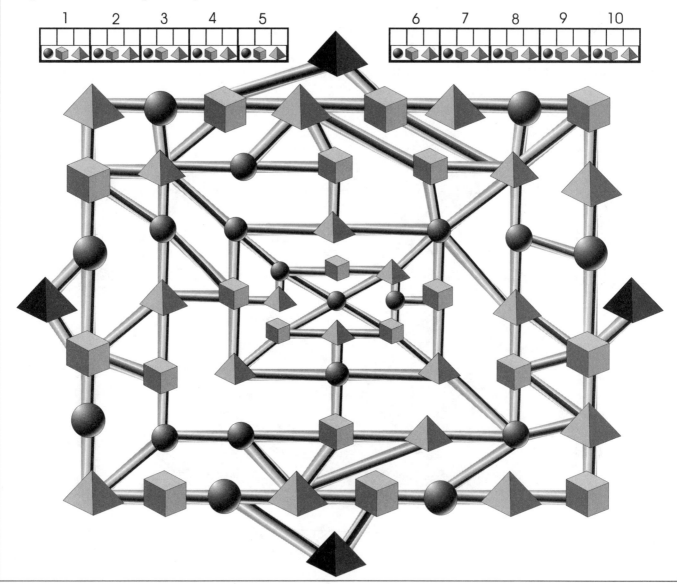

29: JIGSAW SURPRISE

Follow the trail from ball to ball as it passes over and under itself on the cube. Four of the missing jigsaw pieces may help you complete the puzzle. The rest will be of no help to you or anyone else. There is a TINY possibility that one of the missing pieces is in the Parts Store or its Annex.

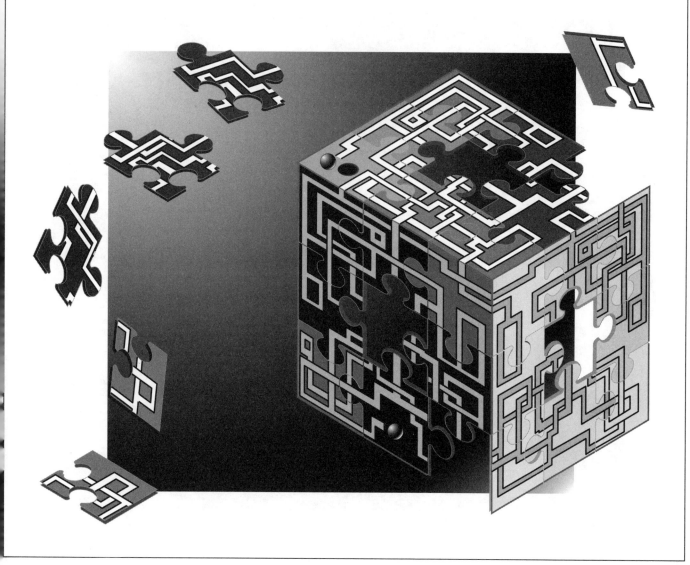

30: JIGSAW BOX

Travel from the IN arrow to the OUT arrow on the path as it wanders over and under itself around three sides of the jigsaw box. Choose the correct missing piece to complete the puzzle. You might check the Parts Store, just in case.

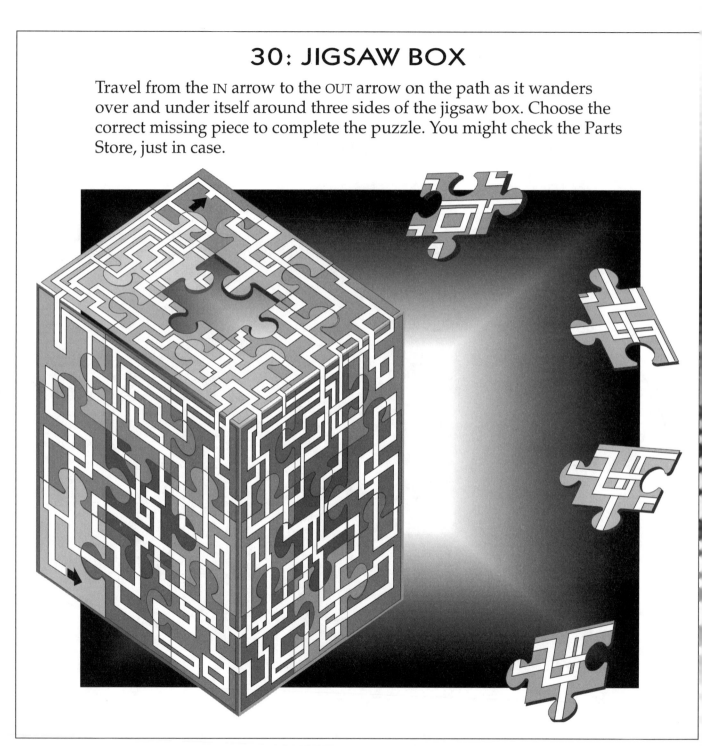

31: ROCK SOLID

This cube has several pieces missing. Some are alongside the cube and some are in the Parts Store or the Annex. Find the proper jigsaw pieces to complete the cube, then find the correct path from the IN arrow to the OUT arrow.

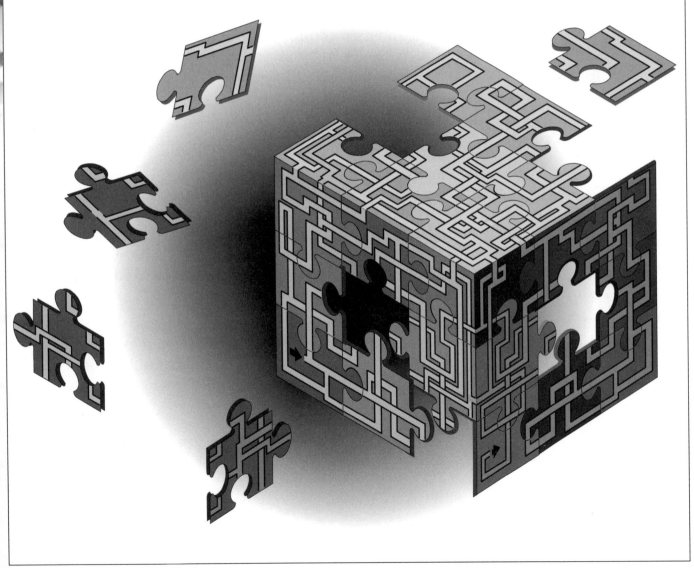

3-D DOOZIES

The following five puzzles will test your endurance, puzzlewise. The problem here is: multiple possibilities. Once you're within the maze you are asked to activate your "jumper" and fly above the page over to a similar or opposite object and then continue through the puzzle, finally completing your task. Now you must remember that the "jumper" was created by a four-year-old, thus rendering any logic you've achieved so far in your life obsolete.

The pathways themselves are hollow pipes that weave over and under each other. This won't bother you because you'll be IN the pipes.

 In describing one of Plato's laws, the Encyclopedia Britannica explains, ". . . it is necessary to regard the numbers which are the physicist's determinants as themselves determinations of a continuum (a great and a small), by a limit and why, at the same time, the one can no longer be regarded as a blend of unlimited and limit but must be, itself, the factor of limit." You can easily see how a person can get hooked on Plato. The next five mazes follow this axiom completely.

By the time you get through this section you will have completed almost all of the mazes in this book. A daunting task at best, but as Plato indicated, ". . . the man who errs intentionally, if there is such a person, is a better man than he who errs unintentionally." Remember this line when you reach the solutions.

32: JUMP BALL

Voyage into the maze by starting at the BLACK ball. When you reach a
GRAY ball, jump to any other GRAY ball and continue through the pipes
to the next GRAY ball. Jump again and continue the process until you
touch all the GRAY balls; then exit at the WHITE ball. You may not retrace
your path or touch any GRAY balls more than once.

33: THE BLACK AND WHITE BALL

Enter the maze at any ball and travel to an opposite (WHITE to BLACK or
BLACK to WHITE) ball. Then jump from the ball you have just reached to
a ball of opposite value. Continue through the pipes, repeating the first
sequence until you have touched all eight balls. Then exit at the OUT
arrow. You may retrace your path as often as you like. There are many
solutions to this maze, so choose the one you like best.

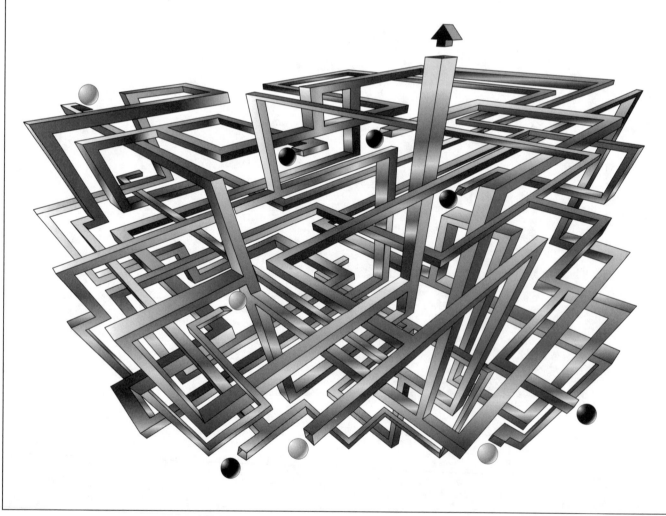

34: WAY OUT

Find the IN arrow and enter the maze on a search for fourteen balls. When you reach a ball, you must jump to another ball of opposite value (BLACK to WHITE or WHITE to BLACK), then enter the pipe and repeat the process. You must touch ALL the balls in the prior sequence before exiting at the OUT arrow. You may not travel over any path or touch any ball more than once.

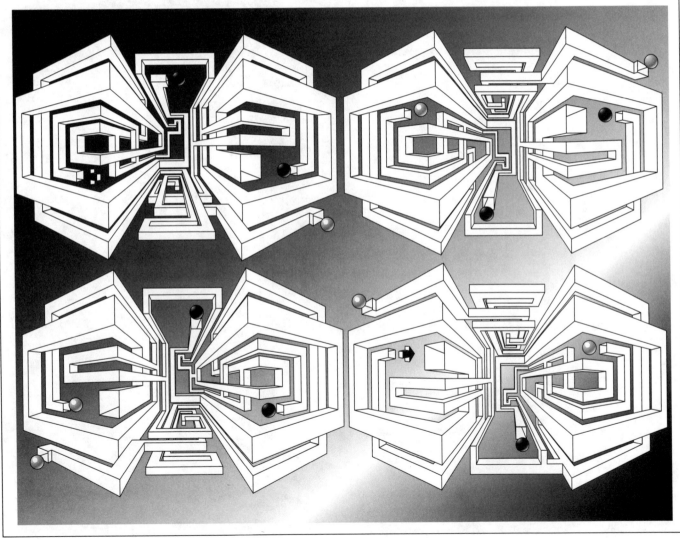

35: CUBED ENERGY

Begin at either a pyramid or ball and travel through the pipes to an opposite object (ball to pyramid or pyramid to ball). Then jump to a similar object (ball to ball or pyramid to pyramid) and travel through the pipes to an opposite object. Repeat until you have touched all the pyramids and balls. You may not retrace your path.

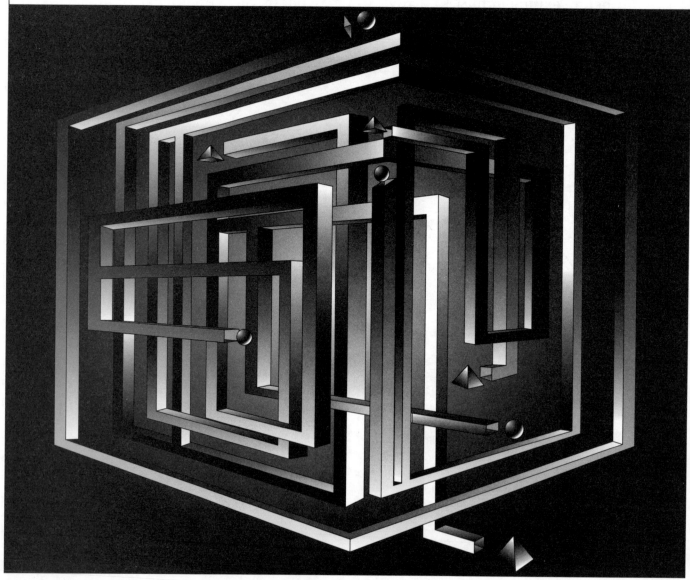

36: DOUBLE TROUBLE

Begin your journey at the BLACK pyramid and travel through the pipes to any ball or pyramid. Then jump to a similar object (ball to ball or pyramid to pyramid) and continue through the pipes until you reach an opposite object. Jump again to a similar object and continue the process until you have touched ALL the objects. Then exit the maze at the BLACK ball. You may not retrace your steps or touch any object more than once.

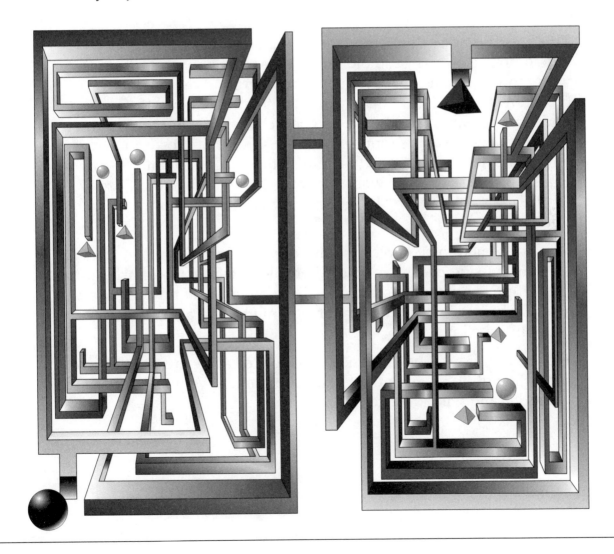

TWO LAST PUZZLES
&
THE PARTS DEPARTMENT

This book began with a common old 3-dimensional maze: a fond remembrance of the "good old days." The book now ends (kind of) with more 3-dimensional mazes, yet another fond remembrance of time gone by. You'll find that even if you're not required to "jump" or find missing parts, the puzzles will be a challenge. I know that every serious puzzler wants serious puzzles to solve. But those of us who only aspire to greatness need a brain rest from time to time. So in honor of all those puzzlers who want a bit of a rest we bring you Maze 37, "Fall Up," and Maze 38, "Tube City." I'm not entirely sure they have solutions!

Now for something completely different. The Parts Store and Annex. All your missing pieces are stored here along with parts of prior puzzles, Hupmobiles, and old broken sticks. When you find a part you need, be sure to look a little farther, you might find a better one! Or, a Bedouin, who knows?

You are not allowed beyond the Parts Store or Annex until you have faithfully fulfilled your oath of maze completion. Venturing beyond is forbidden and will not be tolerated.

37: FALL UP

Enter the maze at either ball, and travel within the tubes as they pass over and under each other. Exit at the other ball.

THE PARTS STORE

The Parts Store and Annex contain several of the missing pieces from previous puzzles. Be careful, however; parts from a vintage Hupmobile may be here as well as pieces from other books and possibly even other galaxies.

THE PARTS STORE ANNEX

If you can't find your part in the Parts Store, it must be here in the Annex. You would be amazed at what people find around here!

38: TUBE CITY

Enter the maze at the WHITE ball and stay within the tubes as they pass over and under each other until you reach the BLACK ball.

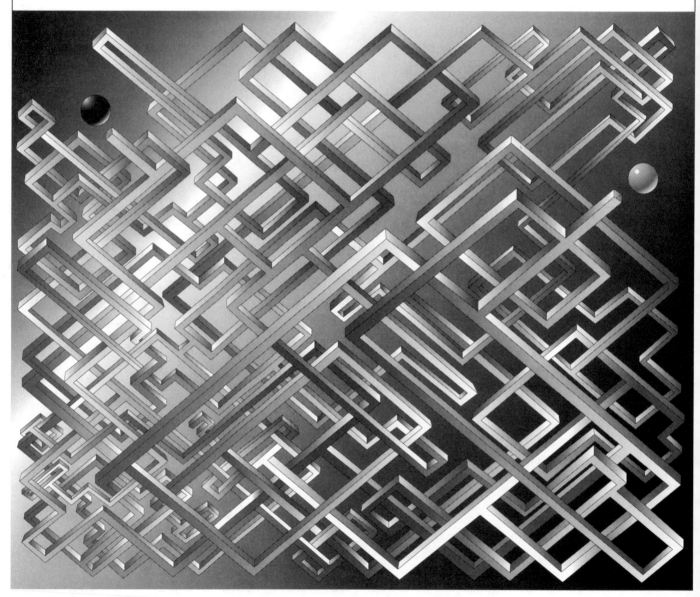

THE SOLUTIONS

This section of a puzzle book is an ominous and intensely personal place to venture. If you're here before you have actually completed the mazes, then you should check your credentials as a serious puzzler. Have you given your all? Did you try your best? These are questions you can only answer yourself. Another question you might ask is, "Would Plato look at the answers before he had completed the puzzles?"

It is true that the puzzle maker has poked some fun at Mr. Plato in some of the sections, but it is out of respect and admiration alone that this was done. I mean, this guy was awesome. Plato lived from about 428 to 347 BC, and that was a really long time ago. He was inclined to become a politician but found at an early age that "there was no place for a man of conscience in active politics."

I bring up the idea of "conscience" because you are on the threshold of the Solutions section. I know it is possible that you, in fact, have done all of the puzzles and are just checking to see if the puzzle maker has a clue. If that is so, then apologies all around.

Please, then, enter this realm of enlightenment.

SOLUTIONS

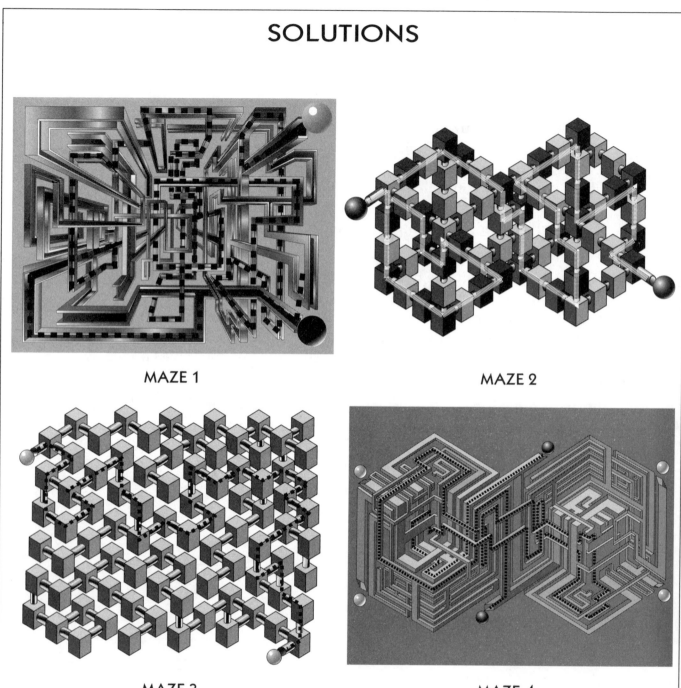

MAZE 1

MAZE 2

MAZE 3

MAZE 4

SOLUTIONS

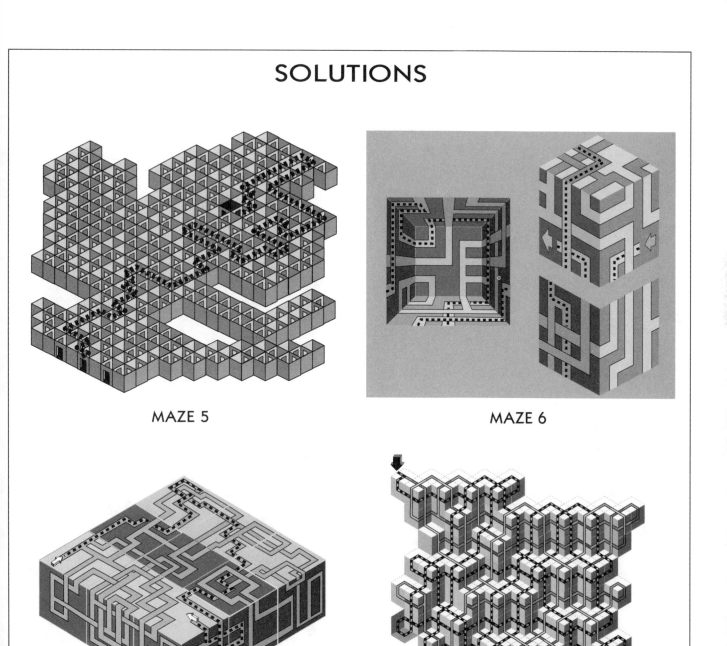

MAZE 5

MAZE 6

MAZE 7

MAZE 8

SOLUTIONS

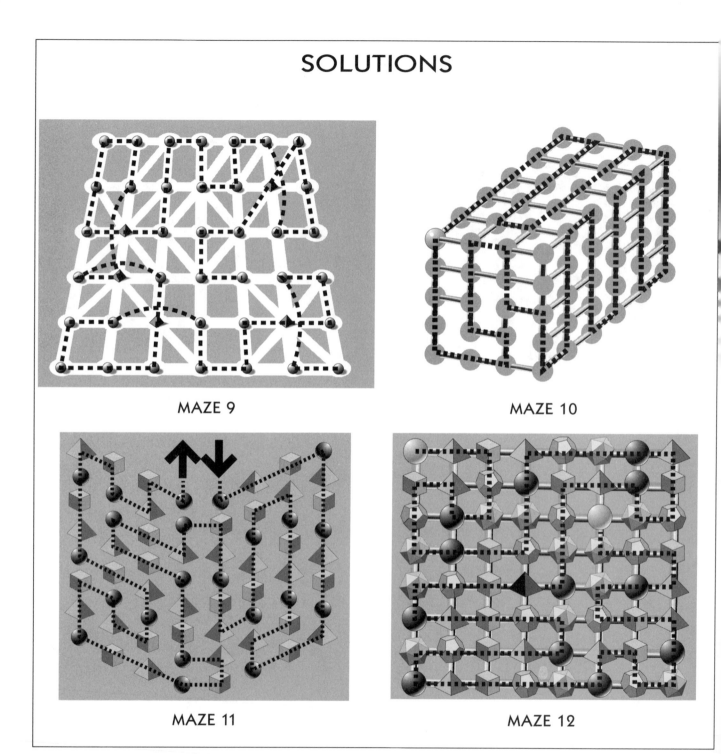

MAZE 9

MAZE 10

MAZE 11

MAZE 12

SOLUTIONS

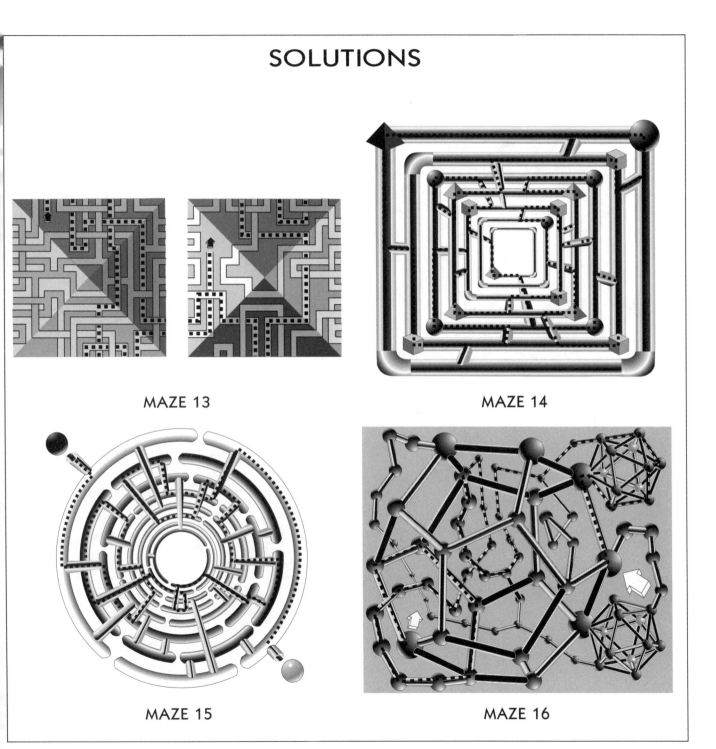

MAZE 13

MAZE 14

MAZE 15

MAZE 16

SOLUTIONS

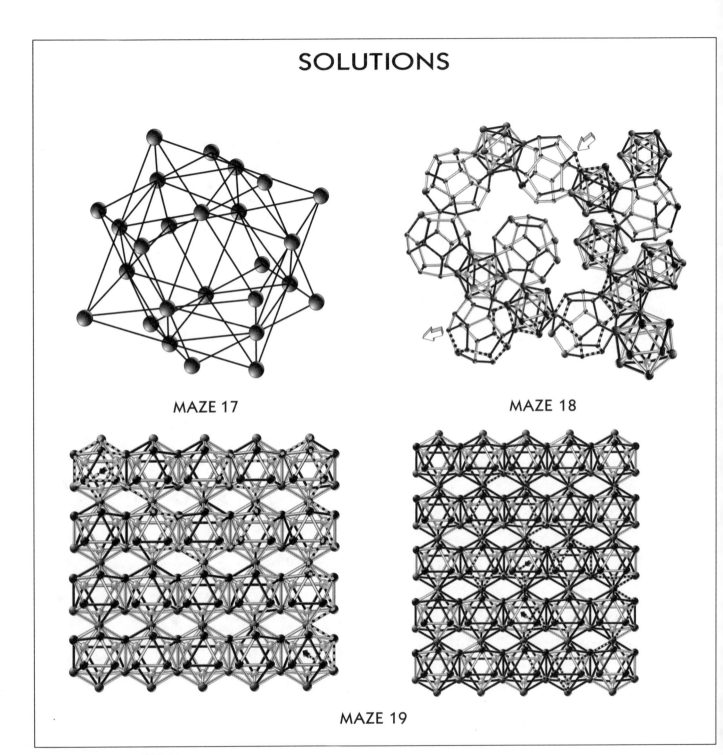

MAZE 17

MAZE 18

MAZE 19

SOLUTIONS

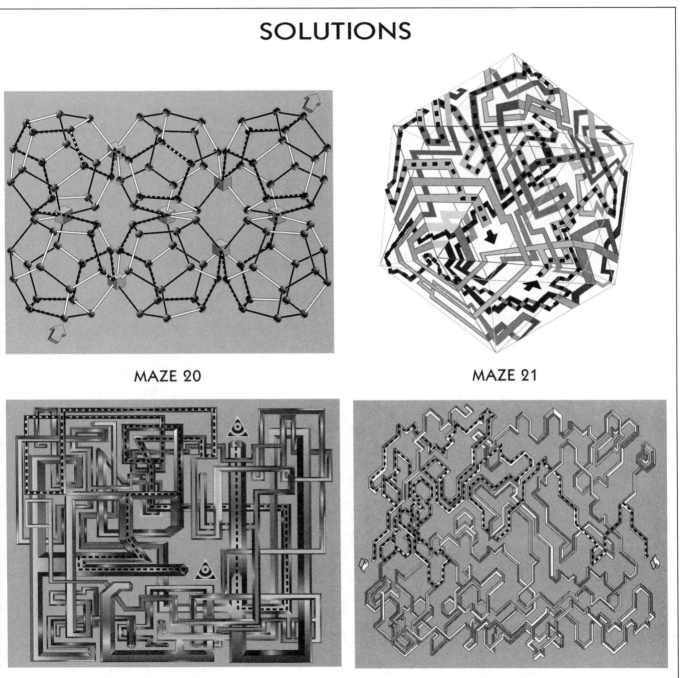

MAZE 20

MAZE 21

MAZE 22

MAZE 23

SOLUTIONS

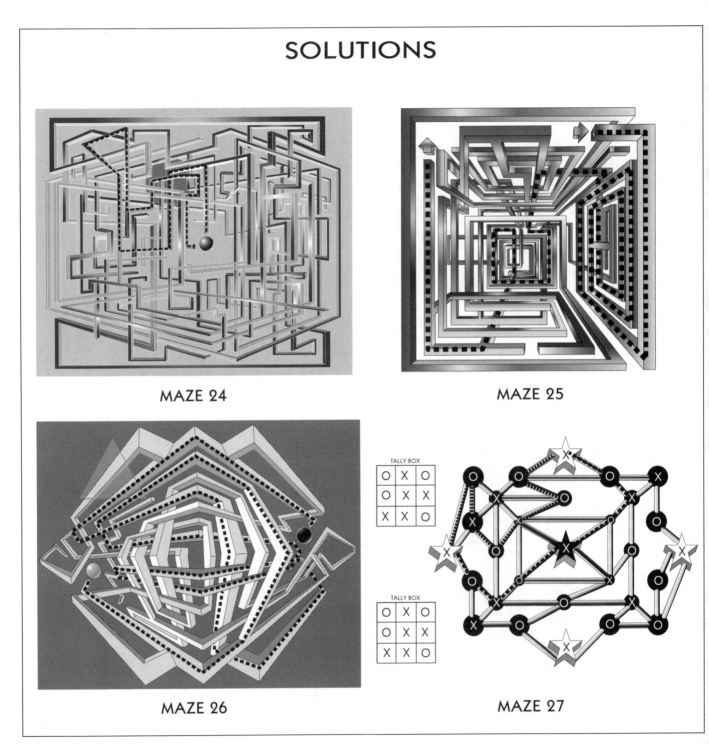

MAZE 24

MAZE 25

TALLY BOX

O	X	O
O	X	X
X	X	O

TALLY BOX

O	X	O
O	X	X
X	X	O

MAZE 26

MAZE 27

SOLUTIONS

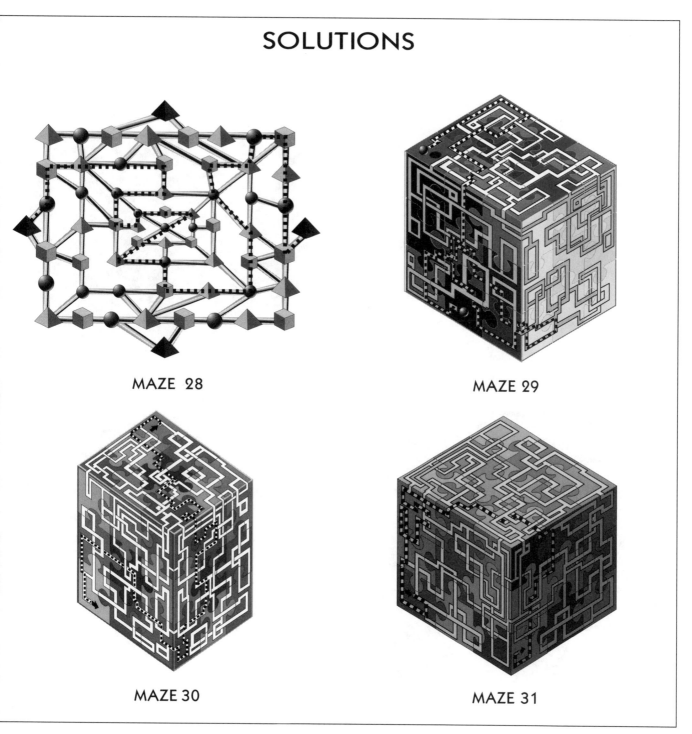

MAZE 28

MAZE 29

MAZE 30

MAZE 31

SOLUTIONS

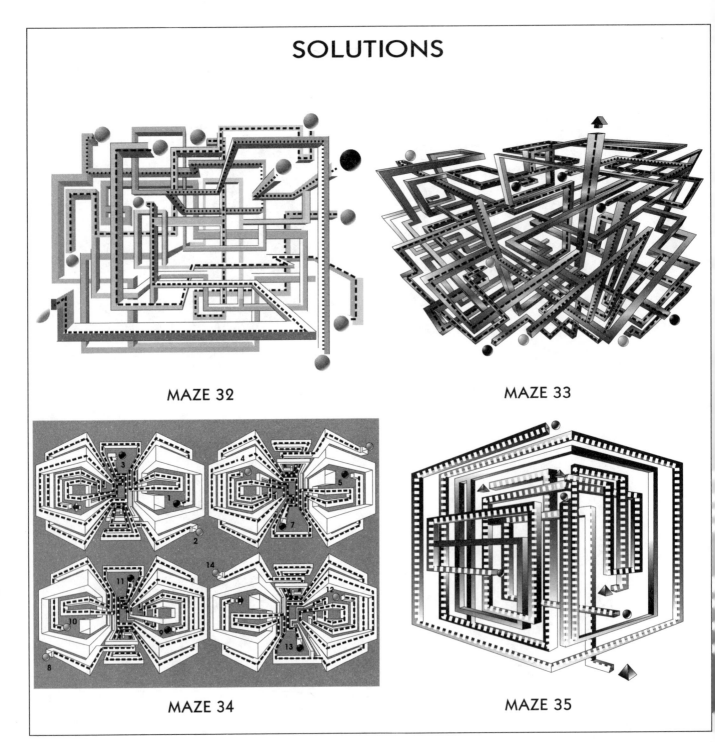

MAZE 32

MAZE 33

MAZE 34

MAZE 35

SOLUTIONS

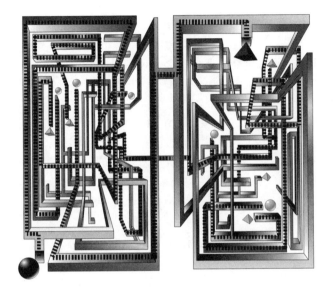

MAZE 36

MAZE 37

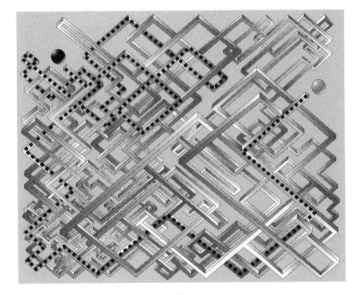

MAZE 38

INDEX

Around About, 38
Around the Square, 33
Ball Diamond, 35
Ball, Pyramid & Cube, 17
Black and White Ball, The, 44
Blow Out, 5
Break-Out, 23
Circle in the Square, 34
Cube Madness, 12
Cube Plus, 24
Cubed Cubes, 8
Cubed Energy, 46
Cubic Hotel, The, 10
Dodecahedrons, 28
Double Trouble, 47
Fall Up, 49

Fractured Fractils, 13
Frog Jump, 15
Hidden Assets, 30
Icosadodeca, 25
Icosahedron, The, 29
Icosahedron Trails, 26
In and Out, 20
In the Beginning, 6
Inside-out Cube, 11
Jigsaw Box, 40
Jigsaw Surprise, 39
Jump Ball, 43
Missing Link, The, 32
Parts Store, The, 50
Parts Store Annex, The, 51
Pipe Down, 16
Plato's Revenge, 18

Plato's Solids, 22
Pyramid Power, 19
Rock Solid, 41
Round and Around, 21
Solutions, The, 53
Spatial Textures, 14
Structure Impossible, 7
3-D Doozies, 42
Tic-Tac-Toe, 37
Try Angles, 31
Tube City, 52
Twin Cubes, 9
Two for One, 36
Two Last Puzzles & the Parts Department, 48
Way Out, 45